AYDEN THE GREAT

Shevonica M. Howell

Co-authors
LaTeisha K. Dean
Audre' R. Caldwell

To order additional copies of this book, contact:
Xlibris
844-714-8691
www.Xlibris.com
Orders@Xlibris.com

ISBN: Softcover   978-1-6698-5811-9
         Hardcover   978-1-6698-5812-6
         EBook   978-1-6698-5810-2

Print information available on the last page

Rev. date: 12/09/2022

This book is dedicated to Ayden Micah Dean

Merry Christmas!

We Love You!

Ayden THE GREAT is a COOL dude!

I bet you are COOL too!

Ayden THE GREAT's favorite
COLOR is dark blue...

What's your favorite color?

Ayden THE GREAT wants to know ...

Ayden THE GREAT's favorite

song is "7 YEARS" by Lukas Graham...

"Once I was seven years old, my Momma told me ... Go make yourself some friends or you'll be lonely."

What's your favorite song?

Ayden THE GREAT wants to know ...

Is it ...

Baby Shark?

Marmalade?

Cool Kids?

Let it Go?

Ayden THE GREAT is
seven years old now, and he
has a big sister that is 10.

How old are you, and do you
have a big sister too?

Ayden THE GREAT wants to know ...

Both, Ayden THE GREAT and his big sister,
have an "A" at the beginning of their names.

A a a A a A a

Does your name begin with the letter "A" too?

Ayden THE GREAT wants to know ...

A a a A a a

Can you guess Ayden THE GREAT sister's name?

Take a Guess!

Is it ...

Allison, Aubrey, Amber, Annie, Audre',
Amanda, August, Abigail, or Ashley?

If your guess was AUDRE'...

You are correct!

By the way,

Audre' rhymes with Marjorie.

Ayden THE GREAT and Audre' have
three vowels in their names.

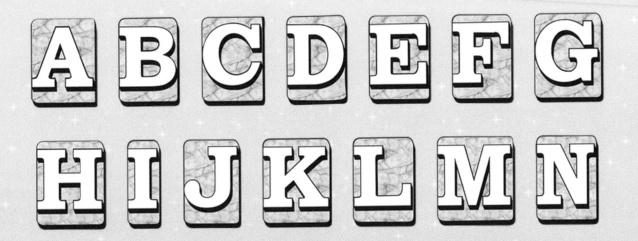

Ayden THE GREAT wants to know ...

Do you know what letters are VOWELS?

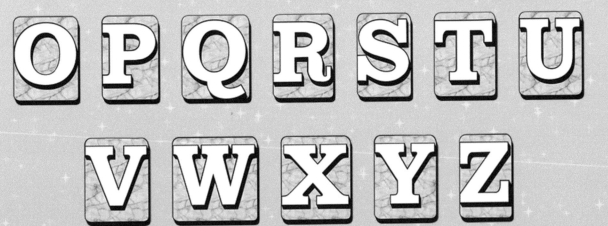

Ayden THE GREAT does ...

Ayden THE GREAT wants to know ...

How many VOWELS are in your name?

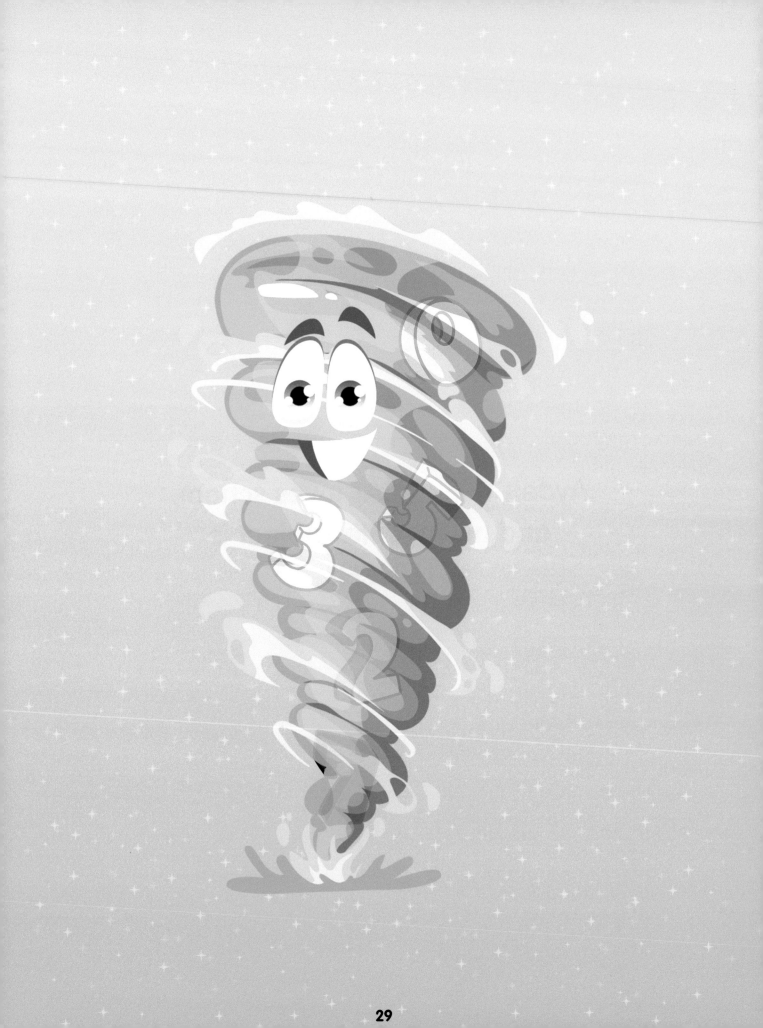

Ayden THE GREAT loves school,
and his favorite subject is
LUNCH!

—dairy product—

What is your favorite subject?

Ayden THE GREAT wants to know ...

Is it ...

Recess, Music, Science, Math,
Reading, Art, History, or Spelling?

WAIT A MINUTE...

SIGHT WORDS

three	is	cool	and	he
with	has	in	are	by
now	the	too	his	school
dark	do	name	that	my
their	big	know	you	it
what	seven	blue	your	color

WORD SEARCH

s	a	y	d	e	n
c	e	u	l	b	x
h	m	v	i	w	t
o	a	g	e	o	a
o	n	o	z	n	e
l	o	o	c	k	r
t	h	r	e	e	g

school   name   cool   seven

three   blue   great   Ayden

too   big   know   age

BOOK REVIEW

1. What is the TITLE of this book?

2. Who is the AUTHOR of this book?

3. Who is the MAIN CHARACTER of this book?

4. Who is Audre'?

5. What letters are VOWELS?

ABOUT THE ILLUSTRATOR

Farrah Milan Prince is a self-taught Artist and college student from Jacksonville, Florida. Ms. Prince is also the illustrator of several additional books and many pieces of her art are being displayed in popular restaurants & lounges throughout the city. Notably, at a very young age, Ms. Prince's art was displayed in a traveling exhibit. Her passion for Art is truly inspiring.

FarrahMilan.com

BOOKS RELATED TO THIS TITLE

2011

Girl, they Ain't ready!

2017

I CAN DIG IT SIS ... THEY AIN'T READY!

2018

What's in a Name?

2020

A Play with Words Word Search

The "YOU TEACH IT" Math Study Guide

2021

We Love You, Dre!

A is for Audre'

Te' Rana Aliyah ... A BEAUTY WITH BRAINS

Finding Myself ... AM I ENOUGH?

**Hi, I'm Jada/Hello! We are
Jarrod and Jeremiah**

ABOUT THE AUTHOR

Shevonica M. Howell is the Founder & Chief Executive Officer of Academy of Scholars, Inc., a K-12th grade private school and nonprofit organization, located in Jacksonville, FL. Ms. Howell is a decorated Army veteran, motivational speaker, and an advocate for student success. Ms. Howell's books are written to motivate, educate, and inspire change.

ShevonicaMHowell@gmail.com

Printed in the United States
by Baker & Taylor Publisher Services